Unicorns JUMBO Colouring Book

www.alligatorbooks.co.uk

© 2023 Alligator Products Ltd.

Published in 2023 by Alligator Products Ltd.

UK Address:
Alligator Products Ltd.
2nd Floor, 314 Regents Park Road,
London N3 2JX.

EU Address:
Calle Arquitecto Francisco Casas Nº 10
Apto. Sa Vinya T101
07181 Bendinat - Calviá
Baleares - Spain

Printed in China. 2024

Magically Appear!

Use your magical artist skills to trace over this
Unicorn before it disappears.

Picture Perfect!

Can you draw who is playing in front of the beautiful castle?

Odd One Out

All these pictures look the same but one is the odd one out.
Can you spot which one?

a

b

c

d

e

f

Bit of Magic!

Use your artistic skills to trace over this
picture and see who magically appears.

Magical Surprise!

The fairy is using her magic to make a beautiful surprise appear.
Can you draw what it is?

Odd One Out

All these pictures look the same but one is the odd one out.
Can you spot which one?

a

b

c

d

Rainbow Magic!

Who is playing under the rainbows?
Trace over this picture to see who it is.

High Jump!

Can you draw what the Unicorn is jumping over?

Royal Meeting!

Can you draw who the Unicorn is meeting?

Odd One Out

All these pictures look the same but one is the odd one out.
Can you spot which one?

a

b

c

d

e

f